P9-EEU-154

 HMH

math
expressions

Dr. Karen C. Fuson

Homework and Remembering | Grade 2
Volume 1

 This material is based upon work supported by the
National Science Foundation
under Grant Numbers
ESI-9816320, REC-9806020, and RED-935373.

Any opinions, findings, and conclusions, or recommendations expressed in this material
are those of the author and do not necessarily reflect the views of the National Science Foundation.

1 Write two equations for each Math Mountain.

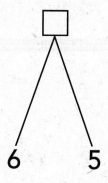
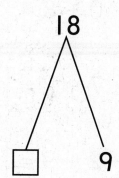
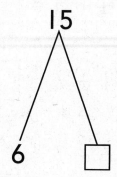

_____   _____   _____

_____   _____   _____

2 Draw a Math Mountain and write one more equation.

$5 + 8 = \boxed{}$ $17 - 8 = \boxed{}$ $7 + \boxed{} = 12$

_____   _____   _____

Add.

1) $4 + 5 = \boxed{}$ $0 + 8 = \boxed{}$ $3 + 2 = \boxed{}$

2) $1 + 7 = \boxed{}$ $7 + 2 = \boxed{}$ $2 + 1 = \boxed{}$

3) $6 + 7 = \boxed{}$ $2 + 9 = \boxed{}$ $7 + 7 = \boxed{}$

4) $8 + 9 = \boxed{}$ $4 + 7 = \boxed{}$ $1 + 9 = \boxed{}$

Subtract.

5) $8 - 5 = \boxed{}$ $5 - 5 = \boxed{}$ $4 - 1 = \boxed{}$

6) $6 - 2 = \boxed{}$ $9 - 6 = \boxed{}$ $5 - 3 = \boxed{}$

7) $14 - 7 = \boxed{}$ $5 - 0 = \boxed{}$ $18 - 9 = \boxed{}$

8) $16 - 9 = \boxed{}$ $14 - 6 = \boxed{}$ $15 - 8 = \boxed{}$

9) **Stretch Your Thinking** The yard sale records got wet. Write the numbers that should be in the table.

Item	Number Sold Each Day		
	Saturday	Sunday	Total
Birdhouse	1	6	
Potholder	4		9
Picture Frame	2		10

    Represent Addition and Subtraction

> Complete the Math Mountains and equations.

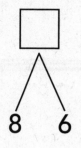

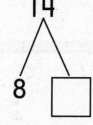

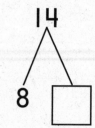

$8 + 6 = \boxed{}$

$8 + \boxed{} = 14$

$14 - 8 = \boxed{}$

> **Create and Solve** Write and solve a word problem for one of the equations above.

_____

_____

_____

_____

---

3 **Draw a Picture and Explain** Draw two different Math Mountains with a total of 12. Explain why you can make two different Math Mountains.

_____

_____

_____

_____

Add.

1 2 + 6 = ☐   5 + 1 = ☐   8 + 1 = ☐

2 8 + 7 = ☐   7 + 5 = ☐   8 + 8 = ☐

Subtract.

3 9 − 3 = ☐   4 − 2 = ☐   8 − 1 = ☐

4 12 − 8 = ☐   16 − 9 = ☐   15 − 8 = ☐

5 Write two equations for each Math Mountain.

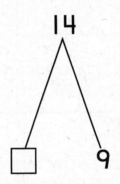

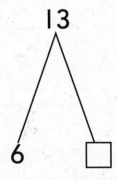

_____   _____   _____

_____   _____   _____

6 Stretch Your Thinking Write four equations for this Math Mountain.

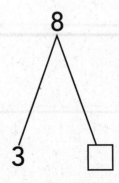

_____   _____

_____   _____

Relate Addition and Subtraction

Make a ten to find the total.

1) 3 + 8 = ☐   4 + 8 = ☐   4 + 9 = ☐

2) 8 + 6 = ☐   9 + 5 = ☐   8 + 5 = ☐

3) 6 + 7 = ☐   7 + 7 = ☐   7 + 5 = ☐

4) 2 + 9 = ☐   5 + 7 = ☐   9 + 2 = ☐

5) 3 + 9 = ☐   8 + 9 = ☐   4 + 7 = ☐

6) 9 + 8 = ☐   7 + 6 = ☐   5 + 9 = ☐

7) 6 + 9 = ☐   6 + 6 = ☐   5 + 6 = ☐

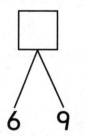

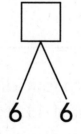

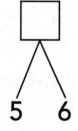

8) **Critical Thinking** Explain how to make a
ten to find 8 + 6.

_____

_____

Name _____

Add.

1
$$\begin{array}{r} 4 \\ +7 \\ \hline \end{array}$$
$$\begin{array}{r} 5 \\ +6 \\ \hline \end{array}$$
$$\begin{array}{r} 7 \\ +8 \\ \hline \end{array}$$
$$\begin{array}{r} 8 \\ +6 \\ \hline \end{array}$$
$$\begin{array}{r} 7 \\ +7 \\ \hline \end{array}$$
$$\begin{array}{r} 9 \\ +5 \\ \hline \end{array}$$

Subtract.

2
$$\begin{array}{r} 13 \\ -8 \\ \hline \end{array}$$
$$\begin{array}{r} 12 \\ -7 \\ \hline \end{array}$$
$$\begin{array}{r} 17 \\ -9 \\ \hline \end{array}$$
$$\begin{array}{r} 14 \\ -6 \\ \hline \end{array}$$
$$\begin{array}{r} 15 \\ -7 \\ \hline \end{array}$$
$$\begin{array}{r} 16 \\ -8 \\ \hline \end{array}$$

3 Write two equations for each Math Mountain.

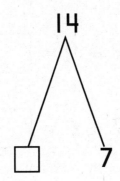
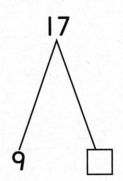

_____   _____   _____

_____   _____   _____

4 **Stretch Your Thinking** Write four different
Math Mountains with a total of 11.

Make-a-Ten Strategies

$$8 + \boxed{6} = 14 \text{ or } 14 - 8 = \boxed{6}$$

Already   8 $\overset{\bullet}{9}$ $\overset{\bullet}{10}$ + 4 more | Already **8**

   or   8 $+ 2 + 4 = 14$

   or   8 $10 + 4$

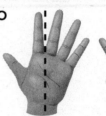

2 more to
10

4 more to
14

Find the unknown addend (unknown partner).

1) $5 + \boxed{} = 12$	$15 - 8 = \boxed{}$	$8 + \boxed{} = 16$
2) $7 + \boxed{} = 16$	$13 - 4 = \boxed{}$	$9 + \boxed{} = 12$
3) $3 + \boxed{} = 12$	$11 - 2 = \boxed{}$	$7 + \boxed{} = 13$
❹ $9 + \boxed{} = 15$	$14 - 8 = \boxed{}$	$17 - 9 = \boxed{}$
5) $8 + \boxed{} = 12$	$16 - 8 = \boxed{}$	$16 - 7 = \boxed{}$
6) $5 + \boxed{} = 13$	$18 - 9 = \boxed{}$	$12 - 7 = \boxed{}$
7) $4 + \boxed{} = 12$	$11 - 4 = \boxed{}$	$12 - 9 = \boxed{}$

8) **Explain Your Thinking** Choose one equation above.
Explain how you can make a ten to find the partner.

Add.

1
$$6 \atop +9$$ $$7 \atop +6$$ $$8 \atop +8$$ $$9 \atop +7$$ $$6 \atop +8$$ $$5 \atop +8$$

Subtract.

2
$$11 \atop -3$$ $$15 \atop -8$$ $$18 \atop -9$$ $$13 \atop -4$$ $$16 \atop -9$$ $$14 \atop -7$$

3 Complete the Math Mountains and equations.

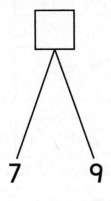

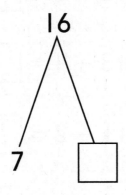

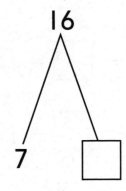

$7 + 9 = \boxed{}$ $7 + \boxed{} = 16$ $16 - 7 = \boxed{}$

Make a ten to find the total.

4 $4 + 8 = \boxed{}$ $8 + 9 = \boxed{}$ $8 + 8 = \boxed{}$

5 **Stretch Your Thinking** Which problem is easiest to solve using the Make-a-Ten strategy? Explain why.

$4 + 5 = \boxed{}$ $6 + 5 = \boxed{}$ $9 + 5 = \boxed{}$

Write the unknown addend.

1 $6 + \boxed{} = 15$ $17 - 8 = \boxed{}$ $3 + \boxed{} = 11$

2 $9 + \boxed{} = 17$ $12 - 6 = \boxed{}$ $9 + \boxed{} = 12$

3 $5 + \boxed{} = 11$ $12 - 4 = \boxed{}$ $7 + \boxed{} = 12$

4 $8 + \boxed{} = 13$ $15 - 7 = \boxed{}$ $5 + \boxed{} = 14$

5 $7 + \boxed{} = 11$ $15 - 8 = \boxed{}$ $13 - 7 = \boxed{}$

6 $9 + \boxed{} = 14$ $13 - 5 = \boxed{}$ $11 - 6 = \boxed{}$

7 $5 + \boxed{} = 12$ $12 - 3 = \boxed{}$ $11 - 2 = \boxed{}$

8 $8 + \boxed{} = 13$ $15 - 9 = \boxed{}$ $13 - 6 = \boxed{}$

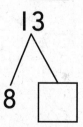   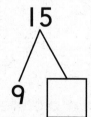   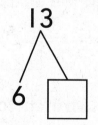

9 **Critical Thinking** Explain how the math
drawing can help you solve $8 + \boxed{} = 14$.

Already **8** $10 + 4 = 14$

_____

_____

Name _____

Add.

1
$$\begin{array}{r} 8 \\ + 5 \\ \hline \end{array}$$
$$\begin{array}{r} 6 \\ + 5 \\ \hline \end{array}$$
$$\begin{array}{r} 7 \\ + 7 \\ \hline \end{array}$$
$$\begin{array}{r} 7 \\ + 8 \\ \hline \end{array}$$
$$\begin{array}{r} 6 \\ + 7 \\ \hline \end{array}$$
$$\begin{array}{r} 8 \\ + 9 \\ \hline \end{array}$$

Subtract.

2
$$\begin{array}{r} 16 \\ - 8 \\ \hline \end{array}$$
$$\begin{array}{r} 15 \\ - 9 \\ \hline \end{array}$$
$$\begin{array}{r} 18 \\ - 9 \\ \hline \end{array}$$
$$\begin{array}{r} 12 \\ - 8 \\ \hline \end{array}$$
$$\begin{array}{r} 11 \\ - 7 \\ \hline \end{array}$$
$$\begin{array}{r} 13 \\ - 5 \\ \hline \end{array}$$

3 Complete the Math Mountains and equations.

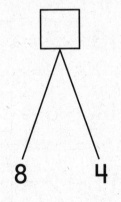

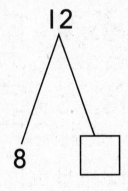

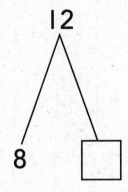

$8 + 4 = \boxed{}$

$8 + \boxed{} = 12$

$12 - 8 = \boxed{}$

Find the unknown addend.

4 $5 + \boxed{} = 11$ $13 - 9 = \boxed{}$ $5 + \boxed{} = 13$

5 **Stretch Your Thinking** Draw a picture to help you solve

$7 + \boxed{} = 12.$

More Practice with Unknown Addends and Teen Totals

Draw lines to make pairs. Write odd or even.

1

_____

2

_____

3

_____

4

_____

Complete the addition doubles equation.

5 ☐ + ☐ = 18

6 ☐ + ☐ = 6

7 ☐ + ☐ = 10

8 ☐ + ☐ = 4

9 ☐ + ☐ = 8

10 ☐ + ☐ = 14

11 ☐ + ☐ = 16

12 ☐ + ☐ = 12

Add.

7	6	9	7	6	3
+ 8	+ 5	+ 2	+ 5	+ 8	+ 8

Subtract.

13	15	17	16	18	11
− 4	− 8	− 9	− 7	− 9	− 3

Draw a Math Mountain and write one more equation.

$9 + 6 = \square$ $4 + 6 = \square$ $8 + 7 = \square$

_____   _____   _____

Make a ten to find the total.

4 $5 + 8 = \boxed{}$ $8 + 4 = \boxed{}$ $5 + 6 = \boxed{}$

5 **Stretch Your Thinking** Draw a Math Mountain that only uses two different numbers. Explain why.

_____

_____

Odd and Even Numbers

Add. Use doubles.

▶ 7 + 5 = ☐   7 + 7 = ☐   8 + 9 = ☐

▶ 9 + 9 = ☐   9 + 11 = ☐   8 + 8 = ☐

▶ 8 + 7 = ☐   6 + 5 = ☐   7 + 8 = ☐

❹ 6 + 4 = ☐   7 + 9 = ☐   9 + 7 = ☐

▶ 7 + 6 = ☐   5 + 5 = ☐   6 + 8 = ☐

▶ 6 + 6 = ☐   6 + 7 = ☐   8 + 6 = ☐

▶ 8 + 10 = ☐   5 + 6 = ☐   9 + 10 = ☐

▶ 9 + 8 = ☐   10 + 9 = ☐   5 + 7 = ☐

Add.

1

4	8	7	9	6	8
+ 5	+ 3	+ 8	+ 0	+ 9	+ 5

Subtract.

2

14	11	18	10	7	15
− 6	− 5	− 9	− 5	− 5	− 6

3 Complete the Math Mountains and equations.

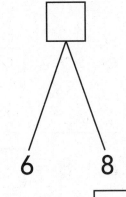

6 + 8 = ☐

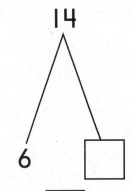

6 + ☐ = 14

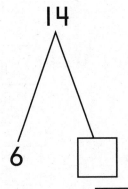

14 − 6 = ☐

Write the unknown addend.

4 6 + ☐ = 12   15 − 7 = ☐   7 + ☐ = 16

5 **Stretch Your Thinking** You have a stack of pennies. Without counting the pennies, how can you know if there is an odd or even number of them?

_____

_____

_____

Strategies Using Doubles

$$9 + 4 = \boxed{13}$$

```
    13
   /  \
  9    4
```

$$\begin{array}{r} 9 \\ + 4 \\ \hline 13 \end{array}$$

I find the total.

$$13 - 9 = \boxed{4}$$

```
   13
  /  \
 9   [4]
```

$$\begin{array}{r} 13 \\ - 9 \\ \hline 4 \end{array}$$

I find an addend.

Find the total or addend.

1)
$$\begin{array}{r} 5 \\ + 6 \\ \hline \end{array} \quad \begin{array}{r} 9 \\ + 8 \\ \hline \end{array} \quad \begin{array}{r} 8 \\ + 3 \\ \hline \end{array} \quad \begin{array}{r} 9 \\ + 4 \\ \hline \end{array} \quad \begin{array}{r} 6 \\ + 6 \\ \hline \end{array} \quad \begin{array}{r} 8 \\ + 6 \\ \hline \end{array}$$

2)
$$\begin{array}{r} 11 \\ - 9 \\ \hline \end{array} \quad \begin{array}{r} 14 \\ - 6 \\ \hline \end{array} \quad \begin{array}{r} 11 \\ - 4 \\ \hline \end{array} \quad \begin{array}{r} 13 \\ - 5 \\ \hline \end{array} \quad \begin{array}{r} 12 \\ - 3 \\ \hline \end{array} \quad \begin{array}{r} 16 \\ - 9 \\ \hline \end{array}$$

3)
$$\begin{array}{r} 16 \\ - 8 \\ \hline \end{array} \quad \begin{array}{r} 15 \\ - 7 \\ \hline \end{array} \quad \begin{array}{r} 12 \\ - 5 \\ \hline \end{array} \quad \begin{array}{r} 11 \\ - 2 \\ \hline \end{array} \quad \begin{array}{r} 17 \\ - 9 \\ \hline \end{array} \quad \begin{array}{r} 14 \\ - 7 \\ \hline \end{array}$$

4) Draw a Math Mountain to solve.

$$16 - 7 = \boxed{}$$

Add.

1
4	8	9	7	8	5
+ 9	+ 8	+ 8	+ 2	+ 9	+ 9

Subtract.

2
15	11	16	9	14	8
− 8	− 3	− 7	− 6	− 8	− 8

3 Draw a Math Mountain and write one more equation.

$5 + 6 = \square$ $9 + 7 = \square$ $8 + 4 = \square$

_____   _____   _____

Complete the addition doubles equation.

4 $\square + \square = 18$ **5** $\square + \square = 12$

6 **Stretch Your Thinking** Suppose you cannot remember the
answer to $15 - 8 = \square$. What could you do to solve?

_____

_____

Add in any order. Write the total.

1 $9 + 1 + 4 =$ ☐

2 $6 + 9 + 1 =$ | 10 |

3 $8 + 9 + 1 =$ ☐

4 $7 + 8 + 2 =$ ☐

5 $7 + 5 + 3 =$ ☐

6 $8 + 8 + 2 =$ ☐

7 $1 + 4 + 8 =$ ☐

8 $5 + 6 + 7 =$ ☐

9 $4 + 3 + 8 =$ ☐

10 $2 + 7 + 6 =$ ☐

11 $9 + 9 + 2 =$ ☐

12 $6 + 3 + 7 =$ ☐

13 $4 + 3 + 2 + 4 =$ ☐

14 $6 + 4 + 5 + 5 =$ ☐

15 $8 + 3 + 1 + 7 =$ ☐

16 $1 + 7 + 2 + 4 =$ ☐

17 $3 + 7 + 9 + 3 =$ ☐

18 $7 + 6 + 3 + 4 =$ ☐

19 $8 + 3 + 9 + 3 =$ ☐

20 $1 + 8 + 9 + 4 =$ ☐

Add.

7	8	9	4	3	5
+ 9	+ 5	+ 6	+ 2	+ 9	+ 1

Subtract.

17	12	13	5	11	18
− 8	− 5	− 7	− 5	− 2	− 9

Make a ten to find the total.

$9 + 6 =$ ☐ $8 + 8 =$ ☐ $8 + 3 =$ ☐

❹ $5 + 7 =$ ☐ $6 + 8 =$ ☐ $4 + 9 =$ ☐

Find the total.

4	8	9	5	4	6
+ 8	+ 7	+ 5	+ 6	+ 4	+ 9

16	11	14	15	11	13
− 9	− 5	− 7	− 9	− 4	− 9

Stretch Your Thinking Explain a way you could add $3 + 4 + 7 + 6$.

_____

_____

Add Three or Four Addends

Make a drawing. Write an equation.
Solve the problem.

1 Brad has 14 toy boats. 5 of them float
away. How many does he have now?

boat

☐ _____
   label

2 Moses collects 17 rocks. He gives some
of them away. Now he has 9 rocks left.
How many does he give away?

rock

☐ _____
   label

3 Claire has 9 markers in her backpack.
Some fall out on the way home. Now she
has only 5 markers. How many markers
fall out of her backpack?

backpack

☐ _____
   label

4 A honeybee visits 7 flowers in the garden.
Then it visits 5 more. How many flowers
does the honeybee visit in all?

honeybee

☐ _____
   label

Name _____

1 Write two equations for each Math Mountain.

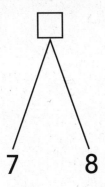   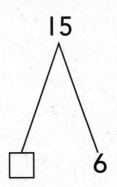   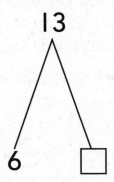

_____   _____   _____

_____   _____   _____

Write the unknown addend.

2 $5 + \boxed{} = 11$ $13 - 8 = \boxed{}$ $15 - 6 = \boxed{}$

Add in any order. Write the total.

3 $5 + 3 + 5 = \boxed{}$ $7 + 8 + 3 = \boxed{}$ $2 + 9 + 7 = \boxed{}$

4 $8 + 2 + 3 + 4 = \boxed{}$ $2 + 6 + 6 + 8 = \boxed{}$

5 **Stretch Your Thinking** Write a word problem to match this drawing.

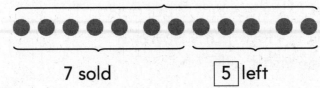

12

7 sold   5 left

_____

_____

Add To and Take From Word Problems

Name _____

Make a drawing. Write an equation.
Solve the problem.

---

1 In the morning, Nick makes 8 animals out of clay. In the afternoon, he makes some more clay animals. Altogether, he makes 15 clay animals. How many did he make in the afternoon?

clay animal

☐ _____
       label

---

2 Carrie sees some birds in a tree. 8 fly away. 5 are left. How many birds were in the tree in the beginning?

bird

☐ _____
       label

---

3 Leon and his friends made 12 snowmen. The next day, Leon sees that some of them have melted. Only 9 snowmen are left. How many melted?

snowmen

☐ _____
       label

---

4 3 lizards sit on a rock in the sun. Then 9 more come out and sit on the rock. How many lizards are on the rock now?

rock

☐ _____
       label

Add. Use doubles.

1 8 + 6 = ☐   7 + 8 = ☐   5 + 6 = ☐

2 7 + 6 = ☐   11 + 9 = ☐   8 + 9 = ☐

3 Complete the Math Mountains and equations.

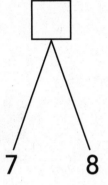   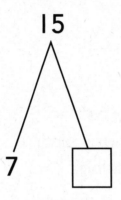   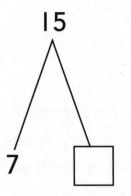

7 + 8 = ☐   7 + ☐ = 15   15 − 7 = ☐

Make a ten to find the total.

4 5 + 9 = ☐   5 + 8 = ☐   3 + 9 = ☐

5 8 + 6 = ☐   4 + 7 = ☐   9 + 7 = ☐

6 **Stretch Your Thinking** Write a word problem to match this drawing.

5 flew away
6 now   7 8 9 10 11   11 to start

_____

_____

Add To and *Take From* Problems—Unknown in All Positions

Make a drawing. Write an equation.
Solve the problem.

1 There are some pigs on Mr. Smith's farm.
8 of them are eating corn. The other 7 are
drinking water. How many pigs are on
Mr. Smith's farm?

pig

☐ _____
label

2 Wendy buys 3 blue balloons and some red
balloons for a party. She buys 11 balloons.
How many red balloons does she buy?

balloon

☐ _____
label

3 There are 14 children at the park. 7 of
them are on the swings. The rest are
jumping rope. How many are jumping rope?

jump rope

☐ _____
label

4 Sean buys 9 red tomatoes and 6 green
tomatoes. How many tomatoes does
he buy?

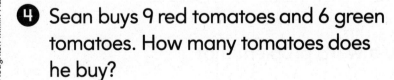

tomato

☐ _____
label

Name _____

Draw lines to make pairs. Write odd or even.

1) ● ● ● ●
   ● ● ● ●

2) ● ● ● ● ● ● ● ●
   ● ● ● ● ● ● ● ●

_____

3) ● ● ● ● ● ● ●
   ● ● ● ● ● ● ● ●

_____

4) ● ● ● ● ● ●
   ● ● ● ● ● ●

_____

Add. Use doubles.

5) $7 + 8 = \boxed{}$ $9 + 8 = \boxed{}$ $5 + 4 = \boxed{}$

6) $8 + 6 = \boxed{}$ $5 + 3 = \boxed{}$ $6 + 7 = \boxed{}$

Find the total.

7)
$$\begin{array}{r} 4 \\ +\,8 \\ \hline \end{array} \qquad \begin{array}{r} 5 \\ +\,8 \\ \hline \end{array} \qquad \begin{array}{r} 9 \\ +\,9 \\ \hline \end{array} \qquad \begin{array}{r} 7 \\ +\,6 \\ \hline \end{array} \qquad \begin{array}{r} 3 \\ +\,9 \\ \hline \end{array} \qquad \begin{array}{r} 2 \\ +\,9 \\ \hline \end{array}$$

8)
$$\begin{array}{r} 16 \\ -\,8 \\ \hline \end{array} \qquad \begin{array}{r} 12 \\ -\,3 \\ \hline \end{array} \qquad \begin{array}{r} 15 \\ -\,7 \\ \hline \end{array} \qquad \begin{array}{r} 14 \\ -\,5 \\ \hline \end{array} \qquad \begin{array}{r} 12 \\ -\,7 \\ \hline \end{array} \qquad \begin{array}{r} 8 \\ -\,2 \\ \hline \end{array}$$

9) **Stretch Your Thinking** Write a word problem that uses doubles, then solve.

_____

_____

Put Together/Take Apart Problems

Name _____

Make a drawing. Write an equation. Solve the problem.

1 One bus has 6 girls and 7 boys on it.
How many children are on the bus?

bus

☐ _____
label

2 Pang buys some oranges. Bill buys
6 pears. Pang and Bill buy 13 pieces
of fruit. How many oranges does Pang buy?

orange

☐ _____
label

3 Davant has 16 birds. He has 7 parrots.
The rest are canaries. How many
canaries does Davant have?

canary

☐ _____
label

4 Complete the diagram by adding at
least two things in the circle.
Write the group name.

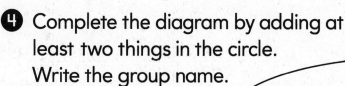
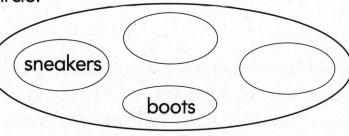

sneakers

boots

_____
Group Name

Make a ten to find the total.

1 $9 + 5 = \boxed{}$ $\qquad$ $4 + 9 = \boxed{}$ $\qquad$ $8 + 5 = \boxed{}$

2 $8 + 6 = \boxed{}$ $\qquad$ $7 + 7 = \boxed{}$ $\qquad$ $4 + 8 = \boxed{}$

Find the unknown addend.

3 $7 + \boxed{} = 13$ $\qquad$ $17 - 8 = \boxed{}$ $\qquad$ $9 - 7 = \boxed{}$

Make a drawing. Write an equation. Solve the problem.

4 Jim has a box of crayons. He pulls out
8 crayons. 7 are left. How many crayons
were in the box to start?

$\boxed{}$ _____
label

5 Tanya has 9 tulips in a vase. She adds
5 more tulips to the vase. How many
tulips are in the vase now?

$\boxed{}$ _____
label

6 **Stretch Your Thinking** Write an addition and
a subtraction equation you could use to solve this
problem: Jill has 6 pens. Ian has some pens.
Together they have 14 pens. How many pens does
Ian have?

_____ $\qquad$ _____

© Houghton Mifflin Harcourt Publishing Company

Name _____

Make a matching drawing or draw comparison bars.
Solve the problem.

① Peter has 13 eggs. Joe has 4 fewer eggs than
Peter. How many eggs does Joe have?

eggs

☐ _____
　　　　label

② I want to give each of my 14 friends an
apple. I have 8 apples in my basket.
How many more apples do I need to
pick to give each friend an apple?

basket

☐ _____
　　　　label

③ Lë has 5 lemons. Tina has 7 more lemons
than Lë. How many lemons does Tina have?

lemon

☐ _____
　　　　label

Write Your Own Complete this word problem.
Draw comparison bars and solve.

④ I have 12 _____.

My friend has _____ fewer

_____ than I have. How many

_____ does my friend have?

☐ _____
　　　　label

Name _____

1 Complete the Math Mountains and equations.

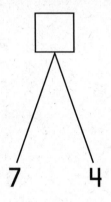
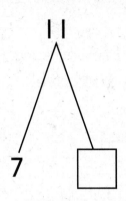
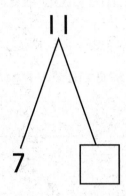

7 + 4 = ☐   7 + ☐ = 11   11 − 7 = ☐

Find the unknown addend.

2 7 + ☐ = 15   13 − ☐ = 5   9 + ☐ = 15

3 3 + ☐ = 9   13 − ☐ = 6   8 + ☐ = 11

Make a drawing. Write an equation.
Solve the problem.

4 A table has 16 glasses on it. 7 of the
glasses are large. The rest are small.
How many glasses are small?

☐ _____
        label

5 **Stretch Your Thinking** Write a word problem to
match this comparison bar drawing, then solve.

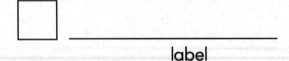

_____

_____

Compare Word Problems

Name _____

Make a drawing. Write an equation.
Solve the problem.

1 Parker and Natu go to the store to buy
sunglasses. Parker pays $9 for his
sunglasses. Natu pays $6 more than
Parker. How much does Natu pay for
his sunglasses?

sunglasses

☐ _____
        label

2 A small ball costs 8 cents. A ring costs
8 more cents than the small ball.
How many cents does a ring cost?

ring

☐ _____
        label

3 If Jared gives away 4 strawberries, he
will have as many strawberries as Phil. Jared
has 11 strawberries. How many strawberries
does Phil have?

strawberries

☐ _____
        label

4 Andrew has 11 soccer balls. William has
3 soccer balls. How many fewer soccer
balls does William have than Andrew?

soccer ball

☐ _____
        label

Add.

1
$\begin{array}{r} 5 \\ + 6 \\ \hline \end{array}$ $\begin{array}{r} 9 \\ + 3 \\ \hline \end{array}$ $\begin{array}{r} 8 \\ + 3 \\ \hline \end{array}$ $\begin{array}{r} 2 \\ + 9 \\ \hline \end{array}$ $\begin{array}{r} 6 \\ + 6 \\ \hline \end{array}$ $\begin{array}{r} 8 \\ + 6 \\ \hline \end{array}$

Make a drawing. Write an equation.
Solve the problem.

2 Jamie has some grapes on her plate.
Tom has 9 grapes. Together, Jamie and
Tom have 14 grapes. How many grapes
does Jamie have?

☐ _____
   label

3 Complete the diagram by adding at least two
things in the circle. Write the group name.

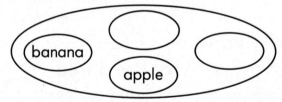

_____
Group Name

4 **Stretch Your Thinking** Write a word problem
that would have the top comparison bar
with a question mark in it. Then solve using a
comparison bar drawing.

_____

_____

_____

More *Compare* Word Problems

Make a drawing. Write an equation.
Solve the problem.

Show your work.

---

1 Susan rides her bicycle for 14 blocks.
Awan rides his bicycle for 8 blocks.
How many fewer blocks does Awan ride
than Susan?

bicycle

☐ _____
label

---

2 Eden has 7 blackberries. Her father gives
her 9 more. How many blackberries does
Eden have now?

blackberries

☐ _____
label

---

3 There were 9 children on the bus.
At the first bus stop, some children
get off. 7 children are still on the bus.
How many children got off at the
first bus stop?

bus stop

☐ _____
label

---

4 The clown has 12 red balloons. He has 4 blue
balloons. How many more red balloons than
blue balloons does he have?

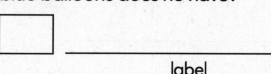
balloons

☐ _____
label

1 Draw a Math Mountain and write one
more equation.

$8 + 9 = \square$ $6 + 7 = \square$ $5 + 8 = \square$

_____   _____   _____

Complete the addition doubles equation.

2 $\square + \square = 12$ $\square + \square = 18$

Find the total.

3
$\begin{array}{r} 3 \\ + 7 \\ \hline \end{array}$
$\begin{array}{r} 6 \\ + 8 \\ \hline \end{array}$
$\begin{array}{r} 8 \\ + 9 \\ \hline \end{array}$
$\begin{array}{r} 7 \\ + 7 \\ \hline \end{array}$
$\begin{array}{r} 1 \\ + 9 \\ \hline \end{array}$
$\begin{array}{r} 4 \\ + 9 \\ \hline \end{array}$

4
$\begin{array}{r} 16 \\ - 9 \\ \hline \end{array}$
$\begin{array}{r} 14 \\ - 5 \\ \hline \end{array}$
$\begin{array}{r} 13 \\ - 7 \\ \hline \end{array}$
$\begin{array}{r} 16 \\ - 8 \\ \hline \end{array}$
$\begin{array}{r} 12 \\ - 4 \\ \hline \end{array}$
$\begin{array}{r} 9 \\ - 5 \\ \hline \end{array}$

Stretch Your Thinking Write a word problem
that you could use a Math Mountain drawing
to solve. Then solve it.

_____

_____

Cross out the extra information or write hidden or missing information. Then solve the problem.

Show your work.

▶ Joel has 9 dinosaur cards and 8 bird cards.
His friend Peja has 6 dinosaur cards.
How many dinosaur cards do the two friends have altogether?

dinosaur

_____

☐ _____
         label

▶ I have a ring for each finger of both hands.
I want to buy 4 more rings. How many rings will I have then?

hands

_____

☐ _____
         label

3 Erica had 6 coins in her coin collection.
She goes to a coin show and buys some more coins. How many coins does she have now?

coin

_____

☐ _____
         label

Add in any order. Write the total.

1 $7 + 3 + 5 =$ ☐ $8 + 4 + 8 =$ ☐

2 $4 + 2 + 8 =$ ☐ $1 + 6 + 9 =$ ☐

3 $6 + 2 + 4 + 4 =$ ☐ $2 + 6 + 4 + 8 =$ ☐

Make a drawing. Write an equation.
Solve the problem.

4 Ryan has 8 stickers. His friend gives
him 7 more. How many stickers does
Ryan have now?

☐ _____
        label

5 The top shelf has a display of 12 pictures.
The bottom shelf has 7 pictures.
How many fewer pictures are on the
bottom shelf than are on the top shelf?

☐ _____
        label

6 **Stretch Your Thinking** Why can a problem
with extra information be difficult to solve?

_____

_____

Name _____

Draw comparison bars. Write an equation.
Solve the problem.

Show your work.

1 Morgan sees 15 birds on a bird-watching
trip. She sees 6 more birds than Shari.
How many birds does Shari see?

bird

☐ _____
　　　　label

2 There are 5 fewer trucks than cars in the
parking lot. If there are 8 trucks, how
many cars are there?

parking lot

☐ _____
　　　　label

3 Anh makes 12 quilts. Krista makes 7 fewer
quilts than Anh. How many quilts does
Krista make?

quilt

☐ _____
　　　　label

4 There are 8 fewer tigers than lions at the
zoo. There are 8 tigers at the zoo. How
many lions does the zoo have?

lion

☐ _____
　　　　label

Find the unknown addend.

1 $3 + \boxed{} = 12$ $14 - \boxed{} = 8$ $15 - 6 = \boxed{}$

2 $4 + \boxed{} = 13$ $15 - \boxed{} = 7$ $14 - 7 = \boxed{}$

Solve the word problems.   Show your work.

3 There are 13 dancers in the front row. 7 dancers are in the back row. How many fewer dancers are in the back row than are in the front row?

$\boxed{}$ _____
              label

4 There are 8 birds in the red cage. The blue cage has 4 more birds than the red cage. How many birds are in the blue cage?

$\boxed{}$ _____
              label

5 **Stretch Your Thinking** When would you use a drawing of comparison bars for a word problem?

_____

_____

_____

More Complex *Compare* Problems

Name _____

Think about the first-step question. Then
solve the problem.

Show your work.

1 Bessie counts 5 fish, 3 turtles,
and some frogs. She counts
14 animals altogether. How
many frogs does Bessie count?

turtle

[ ] _____
      label

2 Amy has 6 more blue feathers
than white feathers. She has
2 more green feathers than blue
feathers. Amy has 4 white feathers.
How many green feathers does
Amy have?

feather

[ ] _____
      label

3 Mr. Green puts 5 tulips and
some roses in a vase. There
are 14 flowers in the vase.
Then Mrs. Green adds 2 more
roses to the vase. How many
roses are in the vase now?

vase

[ ] _____
      label

Name _____

Subtract.

1

17	14	16	15	11	14
− 9	− 6	− 7	− 8	− 6	− 8

Add. Use doubles.

2 4 + 3 = ☐   7 + 8 = ☐   6 + 4 = ☐

3 7 + 6 = ☐   5 + 7 = ☐   8 + 9 = ☐

Make a drawing. Write an equation. Solve the problem.

4 Tom has 12 coins. 9 of them are quarters.
The rest are pennies. How many pennies
does Tom have?

☐ _____
     label

5 Erica has 15 stickers. Sharon has
9 stickers. How many fewer stickers
does Sharon have than Erica?

☐ _____
     label

6 **Stretch Your Thinking** Are all two-step word
problems solved the same way? Explain.

_____

_____

Two-Step Word Problems

Name _____

Make a drawing. Write an equation.
Solve the problem.

Show your work.

1 Malia has 8 hamsters. That is 6 fewer than
Sasha has. How many hamsters does
Sasha have?

hamster

☐ _____
label

2 Han brings some sandwiches to a picnic.
He gives 6 sandwiches to his friends.
Now he has 6 sandwiches left. How many
sandwiches did Han bring to the picnic?

sandwich

☐ _____
label

3 15 children are playing marbles.
9 are boys and the rest are girls.
Then 5 more girls join them. How many
girls are playing marbles now?

marbles

☐ _____
label

4 Mike and 3 friends go to the theater.
There are 9 other children at the
theater. How many children are at
the theater altogether?

theater

☐ _____
label

Make a ten to find the total.

1 8 + 7 = ☐   2 + 9 = ☐   7 + 5 = ☐

2 7 + 4 = ☐   3 + 8 = ☐   8 + 4 = ☐

Add in any order. Write the total.

3 5 + 3 + 7 = ☐   9 + 8 + 1 = ☐

4 5 + 4 + 5 + 2 = ☐   8 + 2 + 9 + 4 = ☐

Find the total.

5
5	6	7	6	8	2
+ 7	+ 9	+ 9	+ 6	+ 4	+ 9

6
11	17	14	15	12	16
− 4	− 9	− 8	− 8	− 3	− 9

7 **Stretch Your Thinking** Write a problem that can be solved with addition or subtraction. Then solve it.

_____

_____

_____

_____

Mixed Word Problems

Mrs. Wise and her three children went to the apple orchard.
The table shows the number of apples each picked.

Apples Picked

Name	Number
Mrs. Wise	6
Michelle	4
George	3
Jen	4

Use the table to solve each story problem.   **Show your work.**

---

1 What was the total number of apples they picked?

☐ _____
           label

---

2 Two children picked the same number of apples.
Who were the children?

_____

How many apples did those two children pick in all?

☐ _____
           label

---

3 Use the information in the table to write your own
problem. Solve the problem.

_____

_____

☐ _____
           label

Name _____

1 Write two equations for each Math Mountain.

7   9

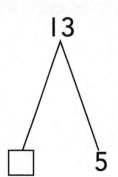
13
☐   5

15
7   ☐

_____   _____   _____

_____   _____   _____

Write the unknown addend.

2 6 + ☐ = 11   18 − 9 = ☐   5 + ☐ = 13

Solve the word problem.   **Show your work.**

---

3 Don has 5 more pencils than
crayons. He has 3 more markers
than pencils. Don has 7 crayons.
How many markers does Don have?

  _____
         label

4 **Stretch Your Thinking** Fifteen children voted
for their favorite color. The votes for red and
blue together were double the votes for green
and yellow together. How did the children vote?

_____

| Favorite Color Votes ||
Color	Votes
Red	
Blue	
Green	
Yellow	

1 Write the numbers going down to see the tens.

1	11			41			71		
2									92
3						63			
			44			74			
	25								95
				56					
		37							
	18							88	
					69				
10	20			50					100

2 What number comes after 100? _____

3 What number comes next? _____

1 Complete the Math Mountains and equations.

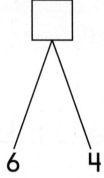 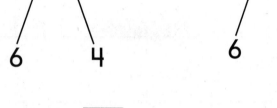 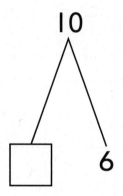

$6 + 4 = \boxed{}$ $6 + \boxed{} = 10$ $10 - 6 = \boxed{}$

Make a ten to find the total.

2 $5 + 7 = \boxed{}$ $8 + 5 = \boxed{}$ $4 + 9 = \boxed{}$

3 $2 + 9 = \boxed{}$ $3 + 8 = \boxed{}$ $6 + 8 = \boxed{}$

4 $7 + 9 = \boxed{}$ $5 + 6 = \boxed{}$ $4 + 8 = \boxed{}$

5 $9 + 9 = \boxed{}$ $7 + 6 = \boxed{}$ $6 + 6 = \boxed{}$

6 **Stretch Your Thinking** Add 2 tens to 100. What is the number? Explain your thinking.

_____

Ones, Tens, and Hundreds

Name _____

Add.

1 50 + 40 = _____   80 + 10 = _____   60 + 20 = _____

   5 + 4 = _____   8 + 1 = _____   6 + 2 = _____

2 10 + 70 = _____   30 + 70 = _____   40 + 30 = _____

   1 + 7 = _____   3 + 7 = _____   4 + 3 = _____

3 30 + 60 = _____   20 + 80 = _____   50 + 40 = _____

   3 + 6 = _____   2 + 8 = _____   5 + 4 = _____

4 50 + 30 = _____   70 + 20 = _____   40 + 60 = _____

   5 + 3 = _____   7 + 2 = _____   4 + 6 = _____

5 90 + 10 = _____   50 + 20 = _____   20 + 30 = _____

   9 + 1 = _____   5 + 2 = _____   2 + 3 = _____

6 30 + 10 = _____   50 + 30 = _____   40 + 20 = _____

   3 + 1 = _____   5 + 3 = _____   4 + 2 = _____

Name _____

Make a ten to find the total.

1. $8 + 4 =$ ☐ $5 + 9 =$ ☐ $6 + 8 =$ ☐

2. $5 + 9 =$ ☐ $6 + 7 =$ ☐ $3 + 8 =$ ☐

3. $2 + 9 =$ ☐ $7 + 5 =$ ☐ $6 + 9 =$ ☐

4. $9 + 9 =$ ☐ $4 + 8 =$ ☐ $8 + 8 =$ ☐

Find the unknown addend.

5. $3 +$ ☐ $= 12$ $8 +$ ☐ $= 13$ $15 - 7 =$ ☐

6. $6 +$ ☐ $= 12$ $4 +$ ☐ $= 13$ $18 - 9 =$ ☐

7. $7 +$ ☐ $= 14$ $9 +$ ☐ $= 17$ $16 - 9 =$ ☐

8. **Stretch Your Thinking** Draw Quick Hundreds, Quick Tens, and circles to show a number between 100 and 200. What number did you show?

_____

Draw Quick Tens and Quick Hundreds

Draw the number using boxes, 10- sticks,
and circles. Then write the expanded form.

❶	❷	❸
176	143	184
<u>100</u> + <u>70</u> + <u>6</u>	___ + ___ + ___	___ + ___ + ___

What number is shown?   H = Hundreds, T = Tens, O = Ones

❹ ☐ ‖ ○○○○○
        ○○

    <u>1</u> H <u>2</u> T <u>7</u> O

<u>127</u> = <u>100</u> + <u>20</u> + <u>7</u>

❺ ☐ ‖‖‖‖ ○○○

    ___ H ___ T ___ O

___ = ___ + ___ + ___

❻ ☐ ‖‖‖ ○○

    ___ H ___ T ___ O

___ = ___ + ___ + ___

❼ ☐ | ○○○○○
        ○○

    ___ H ___ T ___ O

___ = ___ + ___ + ___

Write the unknown addend.

1 5 + ☐ = 15   17 − 9 = ☐   7 + ☐ = 11

2 6 + ☐ = 14   16 − 7 = ☐   3 + ☐ = 11

3 7 + ☐ = 15   12 − 7 = ☐   6 + ☐ = 15

Complete the addition doubles equation.

4 ☐ + ☐ = 16   **5** ☐ + ☐ = 10

6 ☐ + ☐ = 8   **7** ☐ + ☐ = 14

8 ☐ + ☐ = 12   **9** ☐ + ☐ = 18

10 **Stretch Your Thinking** Show 194 two different ways.

_____

_____

Solve. Make a proof drawing.   *Show your work.*

1 Mina picks 63 flowers from her garden. She can put 10 flowers in each vase. How many vases can she fill? How many extra flowers will she have?

[____] vases   [____] extra flowers

2 Luisa has 85 coupons. She can trade in 10 of them for a toy. How many toys can Luisa get for her coupons? How many coupons will she have left over?

[____] toys   [____] coupons left over

3 Dr. Turk wants to buy books that cost 10 dollars each. He has 145 dollars. How many books can he buy? How many dollars will he have left over?

[____] books   [____] dollars left over

4 The track team has 72 water bottles. They pack them 10 to a box. How many boxes do they fill? How many water bottles are left over?

[____] boxes   [____] water bottles left over

Make a drawing. Write an equation.
Solve the problem.

1 Amir had 9 books. He went to the library and got
4 more. How many does he have now?

☐ _____
            label

2 Bella had 15 balloons. Some of the balloons flew
away. Now she has 8 balloons left. How many
balloons flew away?

☐ _____
            label

3 What number is 10 more than 9? Explain or
show how you know.

_____

4 Write the numbers from 34 to 44.

_____

5 **Stretch Your Thinking** Make a math drawing
to solve the word problem. There are 47 children
in Ali's gym class. They need to stand in groups
of 10. How many groups of children will there be?
How many children will not be in a group of 10?

☐ groups   ☐ children not in a group of 10

Combine Ones, Tens, and Hundreds

Make a drawing for each number. Write <, >, or =.

1 131 ◯ 141

2 29 ◯ 28

3 56 ◯ 56

4 132 ◯ 38

Write <, >, or =.

5 157 ◯ 175

6 103 ◯ 107

7 80 ◯ 18

8 100 ◯ 100

9 148 ◯ 149

10 116 ◯ 99

11 122 ◯ 150

12 73 ◯ 111

13 64 ◯ 64

14 188 ◯ 186

Add.

1 40 + 30 = _____   60 + 20 = _____   90 + 10 = _____

     4 + 3 = _____   6 + 2 = _____   9 + 1 = _____

2 50 + 50 = _____   70 + 20 = _____   80 + 20 = _____

     5 + 5 = _____   7 + 2 = _____   8 + 2 = _____

3 20 + 50 = _____   30 + 20 = _____   40 + 50 = _____

     2 + 5 = _____   3 + 2 = _____   4 + 5 = _____

Draw the number using boxes, 10-sticks,
and circles. Then write the expanded form.

4	**5**
153	118
_____ + _____ + _____	_____ + _____ + _____

6 **Stretch Your Thinking** Which number is greater,
134 or 143? Explain. Draw a picture if you like.

_____

_____

Compare and Order Numbers Within 200

Name _____

Solve each word problem.   *Show your work.*

1 Mrs. Green stacks 25 boxes. Mr. Green stacks
37 boxes. How many boxes do they stack in all?

☐ _____
        label

2 Mr. Green counts 56 paper bags. Mrs. Green
counts 65 paper bags. How many paper bags
do they count altogether?

☐ _____
        label

3 Mrs. Green stacks 60 purple onions. She also
stacks 40 yellow onions. How many onions
does Mrs. Green stack in all?

☐ _____
        label

4 Mr. Green sells 39 sweet potatoes. Mrs. Green
sells 18 sweet potatoes. How many sweet potatoes
do they sell altogether?

☐ _____
        label

1 Start with 10. Count by tens to 100.

_____

2 Write the numbers from 56 to 66.

_____

3 Write the numbers from 81 to 91.

_____

Draw the number using boxes, 10-sticks,
and circles. Then write the expanded form.

4	**5**	**6**
127	109	133
$\underline{100} + \underline{20} + \underline{7}$	$\underline{} + \underline{} + \underline{}$	$\underline{} + \underline{} + \underline{}$

7 **Stretch Your Thinking** Add.

$4 + 4 =$ _____ $3 + 6 =$ _____

$40 + 40 =$ _____ $30 + 60 =$ _____

$140 + 40 =$ _____ $130 + 60 =$ _____

Explore 2-Digit Addition

Solve. Make a proof drawing.   *Show your work.*

1 Kivy makes 34 baskets. Her father makes
58 baskets. How many baskets do they
make in all?

   [   ] _____
              label

2 Glen printed 67 posters yesterday and
86 more today. How many posters did
he print altogether?

   [   ] _____
              label

Add.

3
```
  39          67          47
+ 44        + 56        + 98
```

4
```
  48          85          94
+ 33        + 68        + 57
```

Make a drawing. Write an equation.
Solve the problem.

1. Elena set the table for 9 people. Three more people came for dinner. How many people were there in all?

☐ _____
label

2. Hector had 12 pennies. He lost 4 of them. How many does he have now?

☐ _____
label

3. Oni ate 3 cookies that she baked. She now has 9 left. How many did she bake?

☐ _____
label

4. Aisha found 9 shells at the beach. She now has 17 shells. How many did she have before she went to the beach?

☐ _____
label

5. **Stretch Your Thinking** Tisa collects animal stickers. She had 96 stickers. She found 4 more stickers. Then her cousin gave her 16 more. How many stickers does she have now? Explain how you found your answer.

_____

_____

$$
\begin{array}{r} 86 \\ + 57 \\ \hline 130 \\ + 13 \\ \hline 143 \end{array}
\qquad \text{or} \qquad
\begin{array}{r} 86 \\ + 57 \\ \hline 143 \end{array}
$$

$$130 + 13 = 143$$

Add. Use any method.

1

$$
\begin{array}{r} 97 \\ + 45 \\ \hline \end{array}
\qquad
\begin{array}{r} 54 \\ + 39 \\ \hline \end{array}
\qquad
\begin{array}{r} 35 \\ + 47 \\ \hline \end{array}
$$

2

$$
\begin{array}{r} 56 \\ + 77 \\ \hline \end{array}
\qquad
\begin{array}{r} 76 \\ + 88 \\ \hline \end{array}
\qquad
\begin{array}{r} 86 \\ + 65 \\ \hline \end{array}
$$

3

$$
\begin{array}{r} 47 \\ + 73 \\ \hline \end{array}
\qquad
\begin{array}{r} 87 \\ + 49 \\ \hline \end{array}
\qquad
\begin{array}{r} 57 \\ + 48 \\ \hline \end{array}
$$

Draw the number using boxes, 10-sticks,
and circles. Then write the expanded form.

①	❷
185	132
_____ + _____ + _____	_____ + _____ + _____

Make a drawing for each number. Write <, >, or =.

③ 143 ◯ 151

❹ 87 ◯ 87

Add.

⑤ 9 + 9 = _____   8 + 4 = _____   8 + 6 = _____

90 + 90 = _____   80 + 40 = _____   80 + 60 = _____

⑥ Solve the word problem. Ida had a box
of 39 crayons. Juan gave her another
28 crayons. How many crayons does
she have now?

Show your work.

▢ _____
  label

⑦ **Stretch Your Thinking** Add. Explain your method.

$$\begin{array}{r} 74 \\ + 67 \\ \hline \end{array}$$

_____

© Houghton Mifflin Harcourt Publishing Company

$$
\begin{array}{r}
75 \\
+\ 49 \\
\hline
110 \\
+\ 14 \\
\hline
124
\end{array}
\qquad
\begin{array}{r}
75 \\
+\ 49 \\
\hline
124
\end{array}
\qquad \text{or}
$$

$$110 + 14 = 124$$

Add. Use any method.

1
$$
\begin{array}{r}
83 \\
+\ 79 \\
\hline
\end{array}
\qquad
\begin{array}{r}
65 \\
+\ 47 \\
\hline
\end{array}
\qquad
\begin{array}{r}
78 \\
+\ 34 \\
\hline
\end{array}
$$

2
$$
\begin{array}{r}
74 \\
+\ 99 \\
\hline
\end{array}
\qquad
\begin{array}{r}
48 \\
+\ 87 \\
\hline
\end{array}
\qquad
\begin{array}{r}
92 \\
+\ 59 \\
\hline
\end{array}
$$

3
$$
\begin{array}{r}
63 \\
+\ 77 \\
\hline
\end{array}
\qquad
\begin{array}{r}
75 \\
+\ 48 \\
\hline
\end{array}
\qquad
\begin{array}{r}
86 \\
+\ 32 \\
\hline
\end{array}
$$

Add.

① 7 + 9 = ____   5 + 8 = ____   4 + 6 = ____

70 + 90 = ____   50 + 80 = ____   40 + 60 = ____

---

❷ 100 + 36 = ____   41 + 100 = ____   100 + 67 = ____

10 + 36 = ____   41 + 10 = ____   10 + 67 = ____

1 + 36 = ____   41 + 1 = ____   1 + 67 = ____

Solve. Make a proof drawing.   *Show your work.*

❚ Mrs. Martin makes 36 sandwiches for a school fair.
Her friend makes 24 sandwiches. How many
sandwiches do they make in all?

_____
              label

---

❹ Luis has a collection of 58 rocks. He finds
44 more. How many rocks does he have now?

☐ _____
              label

Add. Use any method.

❺   74   58   45
   + 96   + 69   + 87
   ____   ____   ____

❻ **Stretch Your Thinking** Find the unknown addend.

       57
     + ☐
     ____
      125

                    Practice Addition with Sums Over 100

Be the helper. Is the answer OK? Write *Yes* or *No*.
If *No*, fix the mistakes and write the correct answer.

43	OK?	45	OK?	45	
+ 28	Yes	+ 23	No	+ 23	
71		78		~~78~~	→
				68	

1   27
    + 45   OK? ☐
     72

2   68
    + 26   OK? ☐
     84

3   32
    + 29   OK? ☐
    511

4   16
    + 67   OK? ☐
     91

5   59
    + 25   OK? ☐
     74

6   51
    + 44   OK? ☐
     95

7   85
    + 56   OK? ☐
    141

8   58
    + 99   OK? ☐
    147

9   73
    + 82   OK? ☐
    165

Name _____

Solve. Make a proof drawing.   *Show your work.*

1 Sara has 58 flower seeds to plant in her garden.
Her father has 49 seeds. How many seeds do
they have altogether?

[ ] _____
         label

2 Oliver has a collection of 79 coins. A friend
gives him 25 more coins. How many coins
does he have in all?

[ ] _____
         label

Add. Use any method.

3
$$\begin{array}{r} 88 \\ + 56 \\ \hline \end{array}$$
$$\begin{array}{r} 75 \\ + 49 \\ \hline \end{array}$$
$$\begin{array}{r} 64 \\ + 28 \\ \hline \end{array}$$

4
$$\begin{array}{r} 99 \\ + 88 \\ \hline \end{array}$$
$$\begin{array}{r} 77 \\ + 44 \\ \hline \end{array}$$
$$\begin{array}{r} 69 \\ + 83 \\ \hline \end{array}$$

5 **Stretch Your Thinking** Write a 2-digit addition
exercise and find the sum.

Example:
$$\begin{array}{r} 47 \\ + 56 \\ \hline 103 \end{array}$$

Choose an Addition Method

Name _____

Here are some more fruits and vegetables from the
Farm Stand. Answer the questions below. Then draw
the money amount. The first one is done for you.

Apples 79¢	Eggplant 96¢	Pears 58¢	Green Onions 67¢	Oranges 85¢

How much would you spend if you wanted to buy

1 apples and
oranges? _____164_____ ¢ [I dollar] (10) (10) (10) (10) (10)   (10)

$ _____1.64_____   (1) (1) (1) (1)

2 apples and
green onions? _____ ¢

$ _____

3 pears and
green onions? _____ ¢

$ _____

4 eggplant and
oranges? _____ ¢

$ _____

Buy with Pennies and Dimes **63**

Add. Use any method.

1

$$\begin{array}{r} 76 \\ + 38 \\ \hline \end{array}$$
$$\begin{array}{r} 52 \\ + 39 \\ \hline \end{array}$$
$$\begin{array}{r} 67 \\ + 88 \\ \hline \end{array}$$

2

$$\begin{array}{r} 28 \\ + 96 \\ \hline \end{array}$$
$$\begin{array}{r} 74 \\ + 39 \\ \hline \end{array}$$
$$\begin{array}{r} 51 \\ + 89 \\ \hline \end{array}$$

Be the helper. Is the answer OK? Write *yes* or *no*.
If *no*, fix the mistakes and write the correct answer.

3
$$\begin{array}{r} 28 \\ + 66 \\ \hline 94 \end{array}$$
OK?

4
$$\begin{array}{r} 61 \\ + 38 \\ \hline 109 \end{array}$$
OK?

5
$$\begin{array}{r} 57 \\ + 89 \\ \hline 147 \end{array}$$
OK?

6
$$\begin{array}{r} 33 \\ + 67 \\ \hline 90 \end{array}$$
OK?

7
$$\begin{array}{r} 82 \\ + 79 \\ \hline 161 \end{array}$$
OK?

8
$$\begin{array}{r} 54 \\ + 95 \\ \hline 159 \end{array}$$
OK?

9 **Stretch Your Thinking** Doris buys some apples for
69¢ and some pears for 78¢. She gives the cashier $1.50.
Does she give the cashier enough money? Explain.

Under the coins, write the total amount of money so far.
Then write the total using $. The first one is done for you.

1) 5¢   5¢   5¢   5¢

5¢   10¢   15¢   20¢

$ <u>0</u> . <u>2</u> <u>0</u>
total

2 5¢   5¢   1¢   1¢   1¢

____   ____   ____   ____   ____

$ ___ . ___ ___
total

3 10¢   10¢   1¢   1¢   1¢   1¢

____   ____   ____   ____   ____   ____

$ ___ . ___ ___
total

4 10¢   10¢   10¢   5¢   5¢   5¢

____   ____   ____   ____   ____   ____

$ ___ . ___ ___
total

5 Troy has 1 dime, 5 nickels, and 4 pennies.
Draw ⑩s, ⑤s, and ①s.

Write the total amount of money.

$ ___ . ___ ___
total

Add. Use any method.

1

68	
+ 57	

85	
+ 29	

94	
+ 76	

Be the helper. Is the answer OK? Write *yes* or *no*.
If *no*, fix the mistakes and write the correct answer.

2   52
  + 74
  ——
  126   OK? ☐

3   84
  + 46
  ——
  140   OK? ☐

4   63
  + 69
  ——
  122   OK? ☐

Answer the questions below. Then draw the money amount.

5 Dino bought a bunch of carrots for 89¢ and some celery for 78¢. How much did he spend?

_____

6 Tina bought a bunch of carrots for 88¢ and some celery for 58¢. How much did she spend?

_____

7 **Stretch Your Thinking** Draw 10 coins to show an amount between 50¢ and $1.00. Use only ⑩, ⑤, and ①. Make sure it is the fewest number of coins for that amount.

Pennies, Nickels, and Dimes

Add.

1
$$42 \atop + 54$$

2
$$19 \atop + 64$$

3
$$58 \atop + 32$$

4
$$70 \atop + 23$$

5
$$29 \atop + 29$$

6
$$47 \atop + 34$$

7
$$38 \atop + 62$$

8
$$51 \atop + 20$$

9
$$82 \atop + 17$$

10 Explain how you found the sum for Exercise 7.

_____

_____

_____

Name _____

Solve. Make a proof drawing.   *Show your work.*

1 Sal goes to a plant nursery and sees 57 apple trees and 79 pear trees. How many trees does he see in all?

☐ _____
       label

2 Carol has a bag of red and yellow marbles. 48 of them are red and 63 of them are yellow. How many marbles does she have in total?

☐ _____
       label

Add. Use any method.

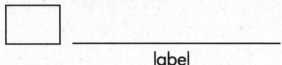

$$\begin{array}{r} 47 \\ + 77 \\ \hline \end{array} \qquad \begin{array}{r} 91 \\ + 29 \\ \hline \end{array} \qquad \begin{array}{r} 38 \\ + 67 \\ \hline \end{array}$$

Be the helper. Is the answer OK? Write *yes* or *no*.
If *no*, fix the mistakes and write the correct answer.

4
$$\begin{array}{r} 57 \\ + 49 \\ \hline 106 \end{array}$$
OK? ☐

5
$$\begin{array}{r} 72 \\ + 39 \\ \hline 101 \end{array}$$
OK? ☐

6
$$\begin{array}{r} 63 \\ + 78 \\ \hline 142 \end{array}$$
OK? ☐

7 Stretch Your Thinking Write an addition word problem using two 2-digit numbers. Solve the problem. Show your work.

_____

_____

Fluency: Addition Within 100

Add.

1 $19 + 26 + 31 =$ _____

2 $25 + 36 + 27 =$ _____

3 $28 + 35 + 23 + 38 =$ _____

4 $17 + 44 + 56 + 30 =$ _____

Add. Use any method.

1.
```
   90
 + 80
```

```
   69
 + 59
```

```
   65
 + 38
```

2.
```
   35
 + 89
```

```
   53
 + 66
```

```
   77
 + 91
```

Be the helper. Is the answer OK? Write *yes* or *no*.
If *no*, fix the mistakes and write the correct answer.

3.
```
   58
 + 86
 ----
  144
```
OK? ☐

4.
```
   71
 + 68
 ----
  149
```
OK? ☐

5.
```
   87
 + 99
 ----
  185
```
OK? ☐

6. Add. Explain how you found the sum.

```
   64
 + 36
```
_____

_____

_____

7. **Stretch Your Thinking** Write an addition exercise
using three 2-digit numbers. Find the sum.

Add Three or Four 2-Digit Addends

Name _____

Solve each word problem.   *Show your work.*

1 Violet returns 4 bottles to the Recycling
Center. She gets one nickel for each bottle.
How much money does she get?

_____

2 Jesse gets 40¢ for cans he brings to the
Recycling Center. He gets 5¢ for each can.
How many cans does he bring?

☐ _____
      label

3 Rosa brings 25 cans to the Recycling
Center. Jorge brings 39 cans. How
many cans do they bring altogether?

☐ _____
      label

4 Write a word problem of your own that is about
recycling and has the answer *85 bottles*.

_____

_____

_____

Under the coins, write the total amount of money so far.
Then write the total using $.

1

_____ _____ _____ _____ _____ $ ____ . ____ ____

2

_____ _____ _____ _____ _____ $ ____ . ____ ____

Add.

3 45
   + 19

4 76
   + 20

5 67
   + 23

Add.

6 22 + 17 + 35 = ☐

7 15 + 39 + 31 + 49 = ☐

8 **Stretch Your Thinking** Darif wants to buy 3 tickets
for a ride at the fair. Each ticket costs 39¢. Darif has $1.28.

How many tickets can he buy? _____

How much money will he spend? _____

Count the 1-cm lengths. Write the length.

1 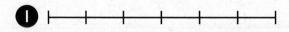 ☐ cm

2 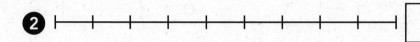 ☐ cm

3 ⟩├─┼─┼─┼─┼─┼─┼─┤ ☐ cm

4 Use your centimeter ruler to draw a line segment 8 cm long.
Mark the 1-cm lengths.

Use a centimeter ruler to mark the 1-cm lengths. Write the length.

5 │ **6** │ **7** │

☐ cm   ☐ cm   ☐ cm

Make a ten to find the total.

4 + 7 = ☐   4 + 8 = ☐   9 + 5 = ☐

8 + 5 = ☐   7 + 9 = ☐   6 + 7 = ☐

Draw lines to make pairs.
Write odd or even.

_____   _____

Add.

30 + 60 = _____   50 + 20 = _____   10 + 90 = _____

3 + 6 = _____   5 + 2 = _____   1 + 9 = _____

Stretch Your Thinking Ryan measures the length of his pen. He places the end of the pen at the 1-cm mark of a ruler. Tell why the measurement will be wrong.

_____

_____

_____

Measure Length

Look for shapes in your home and neighborhood.

1 List or draw objects that show squares.

2 List or draw objects that show rectangles.

3 List or draw objects that show triangles.

4 List or draw objects that show pentagons.

5 List or draw objects that show hexagons.

Name _____

Find the unknown addend.

➊ 4 + ☐ = 12   8 + ☐ = 15   14 − ☐ = 9

➋ 6 + ☐ = 12   5 + ☐ = 11   13 − ☐ = 7

Find the total.

➌
$$7 \atop +4$$ $$6 \atop +8$$ $$9 \atop +4$$ $$16 \atop -8$$ $$12 \atop -3$$ $$17 \atop -9$$

What numbers are shown?   H = Hundreds, T = Tens, O = Ones

➍

____H ____T ____O

____ = ____ + ____ + ____

➎

____H ____T ____O

____ = ____ + ____ + ____

➏ **Stretch Your Thinking** Ian has 2 long straws and 2 short straws. How can he use all of the straws to make a triangle?

_____

_____

_____

Recognize and Draw Shapes

Use a centimeter ruler. Find the distance around each shape.

1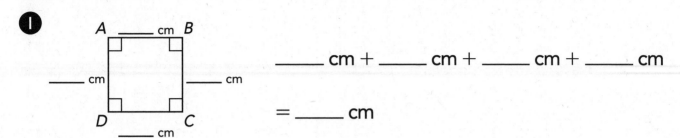

_____ cm + _____ cm + _____ cm + _____ cm

= _____ cm

2

_____ cm + _____ cm + _____ cm + _____ cm

= _____ cm

Estimate and then measure each side.
Then find the distance around the rectangle.

3 **a.** Complete the table. Use a centimeter ruler to measure.

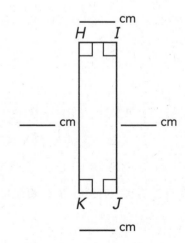

Side	Estimate	Measure
HI		
IJ		
JK		
KH		

b. Find the distance around the rectangle.

_____ cm + _____ cm + _____ cm + _____ cm = _____ cm

Write the unknown addend.

❶ $5 + \boxed{} = 13$ $\qquad$ $4 + \boxed{} = 12$ $\qquad$ $13 - \boxed{} = 7$

❷ $8 + \boxed{} = 14$ $\qquad$ $8 + \boxed{} = 17$ $\qquad$ $16 - \boxed{} = 7$

Solve. Make a proof drawing. $\qquad$ *Show your work.*

❸ Coach Walker gets a shipment of 153 uniforms.
He puts them in boxes of 10. How many boxes
can he fill? How many uniforms will be left over?

$\boxed{}$ boxes $\qquad$ $\boxed{}$ uniforms left over

❹ Use your centimeter ruler to draw a line segment 7 cm long.
Mark and count 1-cm lengths.

❺ **Stretch Your Thinking** Alex has a small notebook
that is shaped like a rectangle. She knows one
side is 6 cm and another side is 4 cm. Explain how
to find the distance around the notebook without
using a ruler.

_____

_____

_____

Name _____

Estimate and measure each side. Then find
the distance around the triangle.

1 a. Complete the table.

Side	Estimate	Measure
AB		
BC		
CA		

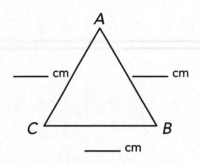

b. Find the distance around the triangle.

_____ cm + _____ cm + _____ cm = _____ cm

2 a. Complete the table.

Side	Estimate	Measure
DE		
EF		
FD		

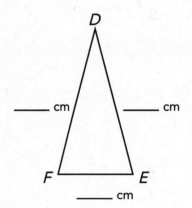

b. Find the distance around the triangle.

_____ cm + _____ cm + _____ cm = _____ cm

3 a. Complete the table.

Side	Estimate	Measure
JK		
KL		
LJ		

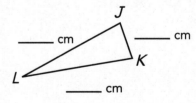

b. Find the distance around the triangle.

_____ cm + _____ cm + _____ cm = _____ cm

Find the total.

1
$$
\begin{array}{r} 8 \\ + 5 \\ \hline \end{array}
\qquad
\begin{array}{r} 4 \\ + 7 \\ \hline \end{array}
\qquad
\begin{array}{r} 6 \\ + 6 \\ \hline \end{array}
\qquad
\begin{array}{r} 14 \\ - 5 \\ \hline \end{array}
\qquad
\begin{array}{r} 13 \\ - 7 \\ \hline \end{array}
\qquad
\begin{array}{r} 16 \\ - 9 \\ \hline \end{array}
$$

Make a drawing for each number. Write <, >, or =.

2 131 ◯ 122

3 27 ◯ 35

4 List or draw objects that show rectangles.

5 **Stretch Your Thinking** Draw and label two different triangles. Each shape should have a distance around it of 12 cm.

Name the shapes using the words in the box.

| cube | quadrilateral | pentagon | hexagon |

1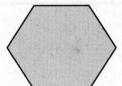

_____

2

_____

3

_____

4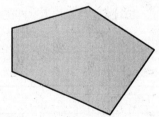

_____

5

_____

6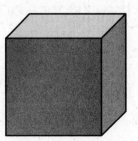

_____

7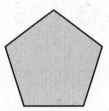

_____

8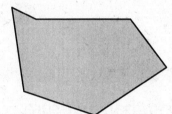

_____

Name _____

Make a drawing. Write an equation. Solve the problem.

1 Tanya bakes 12 muffins. She sells
9 of them at the bake sale. How many
muffins does she have now?

◻ _____
    label

Add.

2   53
     + 28

3   87
     + 45

4   36
     + 79

**Estimate and then measure each side.
Then find the distance around the rectangle.**

5 a. Complete the table. Use a
    centimeter ruler to measure.

Side	Estimate	Measure
AB		
BC		
CD		
DA		

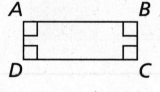

b. Find the distance around the rectangle.

_____ cm + _____ cm + _____ cm + _____ cm = _____ cm

6 **Stretch Your Thinking** Write all the names you
can think of that could describe a four-sided shape.

_____

_____

Draw Using Faces

Name

Complete the table. Estimate the height of six people, pets, or objects. Find the actual heights. Then, subtract to find the difference between your estimate and the actual measurement.

Person, Pet, or Object	Estimated Height (cm)	Actual Height (cm)	Difference Between Estimated and Actual Height (cm)

Estimate and Measure with Centimeters **83**

Name _____

Make a drawing. Write an equation. Solve the problem.

1 Chase has some music CDs. 9 of them are rock music. The other 8 are pop music. How many CDs does Chase have?

☐ _____
label

Add. Use any method.

2   68
      + 35
————

3   52
      + 79
————

4   84
      + 86
————

Estimate and then measure each side. Then find the distance around the triangle.

5 a. Complete the table.

Side	Estimate	Measure
AB		
BC		
CA		

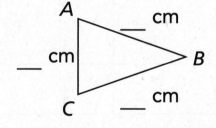

b. Find the distance around the triangle.

_____ cm + _____ cm + _____ cm = _____ cm

6 Stretch Your Thinking Find two items in the classroom whose lengths you estimate to have a difference of 3 cm. Then measure each item.

Item 1 Estimate: _____ cm   Measure: _____ cm

Item 2 Estimate: _____ cm   Measure: _____ cm

Difference between Item 1 and Item 2: _____ cm

1 Find five objects at home to measure in inches.
Choose objects that are less than 1 yard (36 in.) long.
Estimate and measure the length of each object.
Measure to the nearest inch. Complete the table.

Object	Estimated Length (in.)	Measured Length (in.)

2 Plot the data from the last column in Exercise 1 on the line plot.

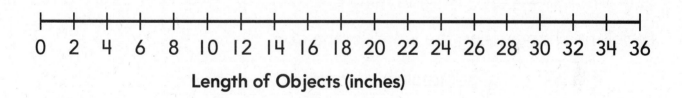

Length of Objects (inches)

3 Find five objects at home to measure in feet or yards.
Complete the table. Remember to include units with
your measurements.

Object	Measured Length (ft or yd)

Name _____

Make a matching drawing or draw comparison
bars. Solve the problem.

Show your work.

1 Erin has 6 grapes. Cody has 8 more grapes
than Erin. How many grapes does Cody have?

☐ _____
        label

Under the coins, write the total amount of money so far.
Then write the total using $.

2 10¢   10¢   5¢   5¢   1¢   1¢

____   ____   ____   ____   ____   ____ $ ___.___ ___
                                                    total

Label the shapes using the words in the box.

| cube   quadrilateral   pentagon   hexagon |

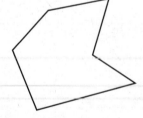   **4**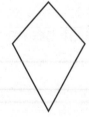

_____   _____

5 **Stretch Your Thinking** Explain why we use rulers
instead of hands or fingers to measure things.

_____

_____

_____

1 Measure each line segment.

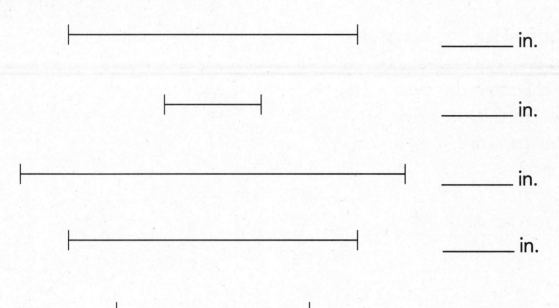

_____ in.

_____ in.

_____ in.

_____ in.

_____ in.

2 Show the data from Exercise 1 on this line plot.

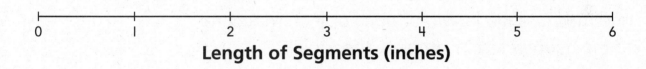

3 Ring *more* or *less*.

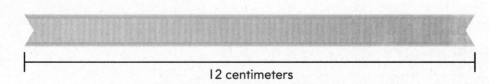

12 centimeters

The number of inches will be *more less* than the number of centimeters.

Solve the problem.   *Show your work.*

① Mya has a stack of 15 cups.
There are 7 short cups and
some tall cups in the stack.
She uses 3 tall cups. How
many tall cups are in the
stack now?

▢ _____
        label

Add.

②   74
     + 15
    ——

❸   47
     + 26
    ——

❹   58
     + 34
    ——

❺ Find two objects to measure in inches. Estimate
and measure the length of each object. Measure
to the nearest inch. Complete the table.

Object	Estimated length (in.)	Measured length (in.)

❻ **Stretch Your Thinking** Juan and Brooke each
measured the length of the same paper clip correctly.
Juan says the paper clip is about 5. Brooke says it is
about 2. Explain how they can both be correct.

_____

_____

Measure for and Make Line Plots

Name

Color the quilt pattern. Use the table below.

Shape	Color
triangle	green
quadrilateral	red
pentagon	purple
hexagon	yellow

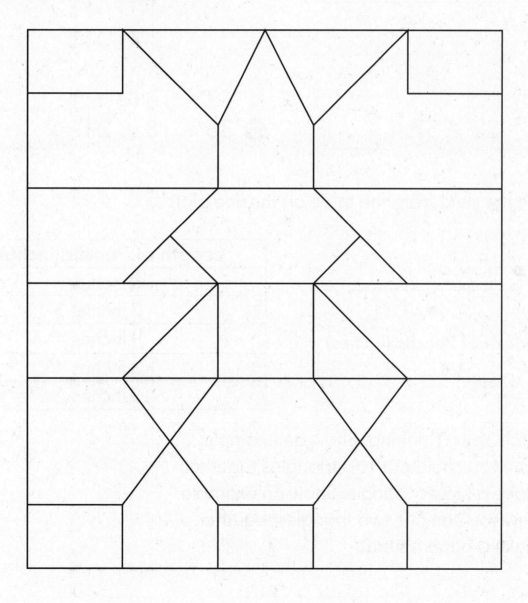

Name _____

Make a drawing. Write an equation.
Solve the problem.

○ Evan has 4 markers. That is 7 fewer markers
than Jenna has. How many markers does
Jenna have?

☐ _____
          label

Add.

○ 14 + 22 + 57 = ☐   ❸ 36 + 18 + 24 = ☐

❹ Show the data from the table on the line plot.

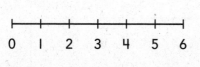

   0 1 2 3 4 5 6
Length of Pencils (inches)

Length of Pencils (inches)
5 inches
2 inches
4 inches
3 inches
5 inches

❺ **Stretch Your Thinking** Show an example
of how you could put two triangles together
to make a larger triangle. Show an example
of how you can put two triangles together
to make a quadrilateral.

Focus on Problem Solving